**Printed and published in Great Britain by
D. C. THOMSON & CO., LTD., 185 Fleet Street, London EC4A 2HS.
© D. C. THOMSON & CO., LTD., 2000.**

ISBN 0 85116 726 8

(Certain stories do not appear exactly as originally published.)

COOKERY

Olive, the Bash Street School dinner-lady, pictured here, may have put together some weird and wonderful recipes, but the Cookery section of the Library certainly has all the ingredients to make you laugh — there's a slice of Bully Beef, a Plum, a Banana(man) and Ham and Egg(head)!

For your first course, here are a couple of slices of Peter Pye, a 1942 Dandy star, who wanted "to cook for the King one day". It took him only eight months of weekly instalments to do it, with the help of some friendly dwarfs and magic cooking equipment!

1—Hundreds of years ago there lived a happy little family in a tiny cottage hidden in the woods in one of the English counties. Father Pye was a woodcutter, while the mother was so fine a cook that she made goodies to sell in the market to help keep the family in comfort. The third and last of the Pye family was Peter, the boy. When he had reached the age of ten his mother and father asked him what he would like to be. Without hesitation Peter answered back:—"I'd like to be a cook, the finest in the world, and perhaps cook for the King one day."

2—His father roared with laughter at his son's suggestion, but his mother was very proud that her son should be so ambitious. She hustled him into the large kitchen and said:—"Well, Peter, if you want to be a cook, I'll teach you all that I know about cooking, then you'll be able to cook your own dinner when your father and I go to market to-morrow." Peter jumped at the chance, and was soon learning the correct way to make pies, tarts, and all sorts of sweet dishes. His mother was pleased with his progress, and realised that her son had chosen the right career.

3—The next day his mother and father got out their old horse to ride into market, leaving Peter poring over recipes written out for him by his mother. His mother gave him some last-minute instructions about his dinner before she rode off with her husband. Peter searched around for a good recipe before he started cooking his mid-day meal, and at last decided to make a plover pie and apple tart, which were his favourite dishes.

4—Soon everything was ready, and the pie came out of the oven covered with a lovely crisp brown paste. There was far too much for the young cook to eat, so he decided to take it and share it with his friends, the dwarfs. The dwarfs were little people who stayed in the woods, living in hollow trees and other cosy places. When Peter offered them a share of his pie they refused, asking the lad if he wanted to poison them.

...that it wasn't poison by eating ... hungry dwarfs didn't wait for a ... into the pie. In their hurry to get ...ghting, but Peter saw that they all ...pie and tart were finished, and they ...st food that they had ever tasted. ... with their praise.

6—But the dwarfs hadn't finished thanking him yet. They scurried off to their quaint little homes, and returned with a lot of cooking utensils. They gave them to Peter, and told him that they had magic properties. Peter was charmed with the funny little men's presents, and he promised that he would make good use of them. He gathered up the empty pie-dish and headed for home, holding the dwarfs' presents tightly.

...a moment too soon. When Peter got back ...tchen, a tall, cruel man-at-arms grabbed him by ...here are they?" he snarled. All around them burly ...carefully searching for their lost prisoners. "You're ...ey cook, aren't you?" he asked, giving Peter's ear ..."Well, start and cook something for us."

8—Peter saw a golden opportunity to trap the brutal knights. With some food-stuffs the knights had brought he set about making them a luxurious dinner. But, unknown to the knights, he added a powerful sleeping draught, which his friends the dwarfs of the woods had given him. The hungry knights greedily attacked Peter's wonderful dishes, and then their heads dropped lower and lower, until they were all snoring loudly.

PARTY INVITATION

Here's your invitation to a children's birthday party in The Dandy from 1976, with ice-cream, jelly — and Bully Beef and Chips!

Sir Coward de Custard, a Dandy fellow from 25 years ago, wasn't too brave, but his companion always made sure he had a better feed than just custard at the end of each story!

I'M HAVING A PARTY, COMING?

UM GOODY! UNCLE WANTS ME TO GO TO UM PARTY IN HIS HUNTING LODGE IN UM HILLS!

LITTLE PLUM

FIDO

I'LL GO TO UM PARTY IN FANCY DRESS!

UM BEAR'S SKIN!

LATER — UP IN UM HILLS —

HUNTING LODGE

WE CAN'T WAIT ANY LONGER FOR MY PESKY LITTLE NEPHEW! LET'S START OUR BEAR-HUNTING PARTY!

KIND OF UNCLE TO COME AN' MEET ME!

YOO-HOO!

?

BUT-BUT-BUT-

Little Plum stories didn't always have much food in them — but here's one from 1957 that has a lot of food, and a little of Little Plum, 'cause he's disguised! 'Bearly' visible, in fact!

SHOOT UM!

LITTLE BEAR MAKE UM TASTY BEARSTEAK!

WHAT A WAY TO SPEND XMAS!

BUT- UNCLE'S HUNTING PARTY AREN'T THE ONLY ONES WHO MISTAKE PLUM FOR A BEAR!

GRR! LOOK, FELLAS. ONE OF OUR COMRADES NEEDS HELP!

YOU'RE SAFE NOW, PAL!

LUCKY PLUM! THE BEARS ARE HAVING A PARTY WITH TUCK PINCHED FROM UNCLE'S HUNTING LODGE!

POOR OL' UNCLE- LUCKY ME!

THE 3 BEARS

In the mid-70s, the Beano's "3 Bears" pied . . . er . . . spied the answer to all their hunger problems at Hank's store!

GROAN! A WHOLE WEEK WITHOUT GRUB!

I'M WEAK!

WE NEED A FEAST TO REGAIN OUR STRENGTH!

LOOK! IT'S LIKE A DREAM COME TRUE!

WELCOME TO HANK'S STORE

HANK'S STORE

SLURP! A GIANT PIE!

ERK!

GRR! IT'S ONLY PLASTIC! IT'S JUST FOR DISPLAY!

WAIT, FAMILY! WE'LL SWOP EVERYTHING WE'VE GOT FOR THIS PIE! WE NEED IT!

IDEA

POOR PA! THE HUNGER'S MADE HIM DAFT!

YOU CAN HAVE ALL OUR BELONGINGS IN EXCHANGE FOR THAT PIE! PLEASE, HANK! OH, PLEASE!

FOOLS! THEY THINK IT'S REAL!

OK! IT'S A DEAL!

So—

THERE'S MORE TO COME!

I HOPE SO — EVERYTHING, YOU SAID!

TALLY-HO!

FUNNY! I DON'T REMEMBER THAT PIE BEING AS HEAVY AS THAT!

Later—

THAT'S IT--THAT'S THE LOT!

RIGHT! THE PIE'S ALL YOURS!

LET'S GET OUR PIE HOME NOW, FAMILY!

DON'T EAT IT ALL AT ONCE! TITTER!

MY STORE! IT'S EMPTY! THE FOOD'S ALL GONE!

PA EMPTIED IT INTO THE PIE WHEN YOU WERE BUSY WATCHING THE OTHER TWO!

LOGS

MMM! THIS PIE FILLING IS DELICIOUS!

BIG EGGO

Big Eggo, the ostrich from The Beano of the 40's, was sometimes a recipe for silliness. Take a look at the ingredients of this story!

Food's a WONDERFUL thing — just ask The Beano's Wonder Boy, from forty years ago!

I wonder what it'd be like t'be...

...an' eatin' champion? Every week I'd break my own world record!

At the sound of the starter's gun, I'd tackle the sausage an' mash!

BANG!

...then I'd munch my way through a pie...

...an' a few apples!

I'd wash that snack down with some pop...

...then I'd have some spaghetti...

MUNCH! MUNCH! MUNCH! MUNCH!

BUT, HOLDEVERYTHIN'!

Supposin' the spaghetti got caught...

...in the judge's pullover...

...an I ate it all up!

MUNCH! MUNCH! MUNCH!

OW! OW! OW!

DON'T WANNA BE AN EATIN' CHAMPION!

CASTOR OIL

Any food section wouldn't be complete without The Dandy's Hungry Horace — seen here are a couple of helpings from the late '40s.

HISTORY

The Beano and The Dandy themselves have both made history as long-lived comics. They have also kept a keen eye on history as a source of funny material, from Robin Hood's Schooldays, to The Jocks and The Geordies re-enacting the Battle of Waterloo — in a library!

You may wonder why Korky is dressed as a Roman charioteer. Turn the page and you'll find the answer.

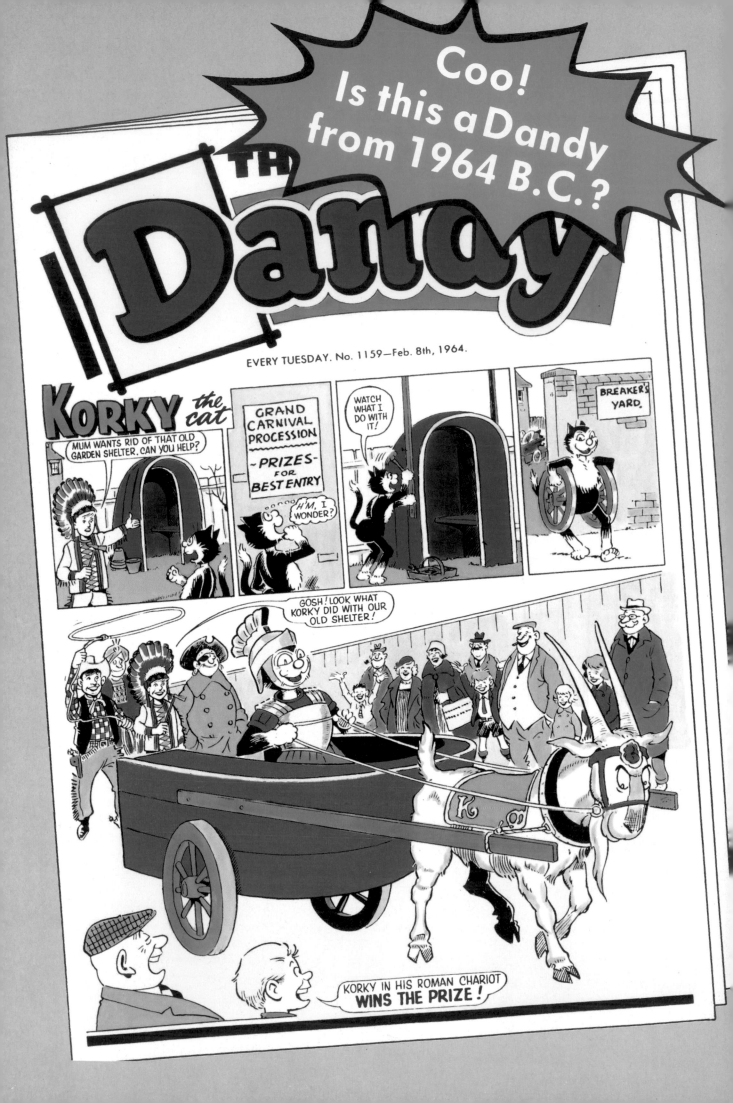

This 1974 Biffo story perhaps created a little bit of history, because it was only seven months later that Dennis the Menace REALLY took over Biffo's page, to become a regular two-page Menace tale on the front and rear covers.

Grandpa was a firm "Beano" favourite for around 15 years, in various series. His origins were never discussed — had he ALWAYS been an Old-Age-Pensioner? When did he receive his first pension? After much investigation, the following long-lost page was discovered in a disused store. This page should provide some of the answers!

This piece of comic history is so secret, the page had to be put in sideways! In 1957, The Beano revealed . . . Roger the Dodger's address!

Teacher of the Bash Street Kids in The Beano has always tried his best to give the kids of 2B some history lessons — which are absolutely hysterical . . . er . . . historically inaccurate, as these examples from 1958, 1962 and 1978 show!

A BRIEF HISTORY OF BASH STREET

— Founded in 1750 (according to Teacher!)

— Losted for umpteen years until first appearance in "The Beano" issue dated 13.2.54 — single page, red-and-black-coloured. The title of the page then was "WHEN THE BELL RINGS".

— In 1955, boys' paper, "The Wizard", printed a series of "Bash Street" stories in text form. (To all you Smiffys out there, that means no pictures, just words.)

— In 1956, the title, "WHEN THE BELL RINGS" was changed to, simply, "THE BASH STREET KIDS".

— In 1962, the story expanded to two pages, in full colour.

— a new, ultra-modern Bash Street school was built in 1963 — but was destroyed by Smiffy's head a week later!

— 1972 saw Cuthbert Cringeworthy, class swot, joining Danny, Fatty and the others in 2B.

— Olive, the Bash Street Dinner Lady, first appeared in 1981.

HERE'S A BOX OF DATES FOR YOU, TEACHER.

SIMPER

THANKS. YOU CAN HAVE THE DAY OFF, YOU NICE CHILDREN!

OOH TA!

WHOOOSH

THUNDER OF HOOVES

DONE!

APRIL 1st

BACK TO SCHOOL!

SEEING YOU LIKE DATES SO MUCH, I'M GOING TO MAKE YOU REMEMBER SOME HISTORY DATES! WE'LL START OFF WITH BOADICEA, A.D. 61.

YOU CAN BUILD ME A CHARIOT LIKE SHE HAD, WITH WHOPPING BIG KNIVES AND CHOPPERS ON THE WHEELS.

RIGHT, CHILDREN EVERYBODY OUT — WE'RE HERE!

CRASH!

YES, IT WAS ON THIS VERY SPOT THAT ETHELRED THE BRAINLESS DEFEATED ALFRED THE GREAT BY TWO GOALS TO ONE IN 1066 B.C. — HARUMPH!

THIS IS BORIN' ME TO TEARS. HOW ABOUT A GAME OF FOOTBALL?

THE GAME BEGINS.

I'LL HEAD IT JUST INSIDE THE POST

GOAL POST

GOAL POST

...AND THESE STONES HAVE STOOD HERE FOR THOUSANDS OF YEARS, AS A LASTING MEMORIAL TO THOSE FAR-OFF TIMES — AHEM!

BONE HINGE

SHUDDER

OOPS! MISSED!

SHUDDER

SHAKE

PUT UP IN 3,000 B.C. THE STONES HAVE DEFIED THE STORMS OF COUNTLESS YEARS AND NOTHING HAS EVER MOVED THEM

WOW! I'M GETTIN' OUT O' THIS!

BONE-HINGE

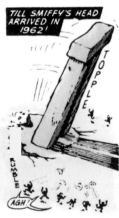

TILL SMIFFY'S HEAD ARRIVED IN 1962!

TOPPLE

RUMBLE

AGH!

WHEN THE DUST SETTLES —

WELL, WELL! WE'VE UNCOVERED A STONE-AGE CLASSROOM JUST TAKE YOUR PLACES, CHILDREN, AND WE'LL CONTINUE WITH THE LESSON.

CAKE

PAY ATTENTION, YOU NIT!

OOYAH!

I MUST NOT FIRE STONY PELLETS AT TEACHER

HISTORY JULIUS CAESAR INVADED BRITAIN IN 55 B.C.

ANCIENT BRITON

ROMAN EAGLE

BOADICEA

JULIUS CAESAR

WHY DID I EVER TAKE UP TEACHING?

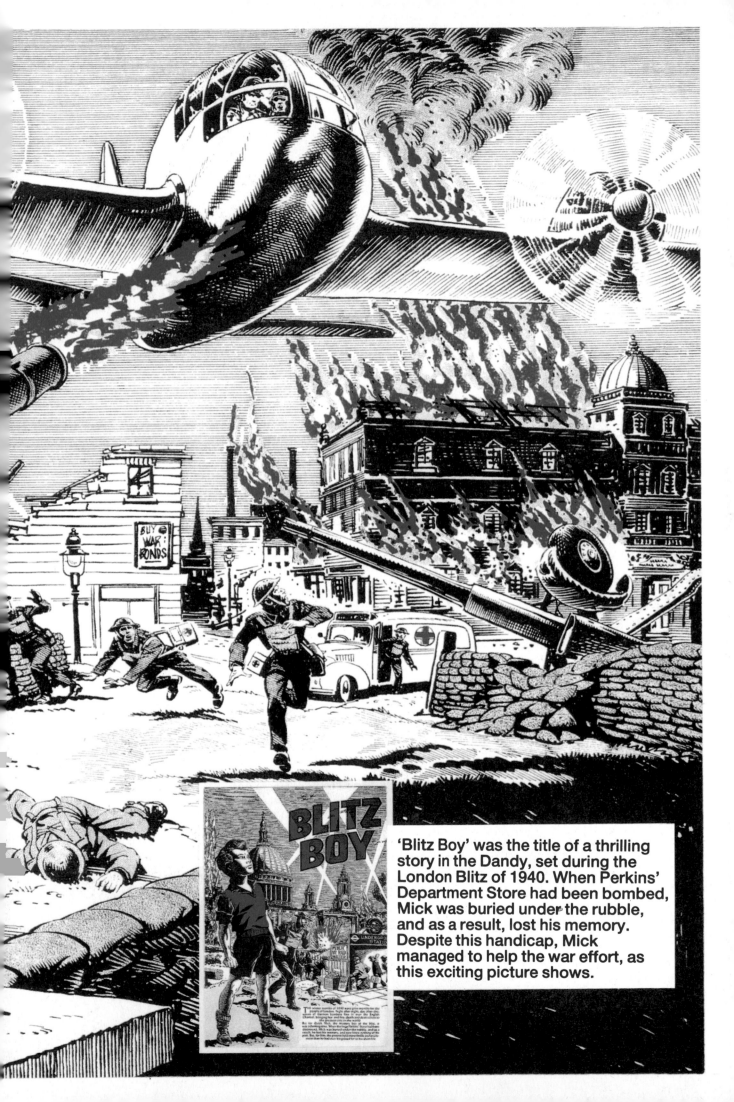

'Blitz Boy' was the title of a thrilling story in the Dandy, set during the London Blitz of 1940. When Perkins' Department Store had been bombed, Mick was buried under the rubble, and as a result, lost his memory. Despite this handicap, Mick managed to help the war effort, as this exciting picture shows.

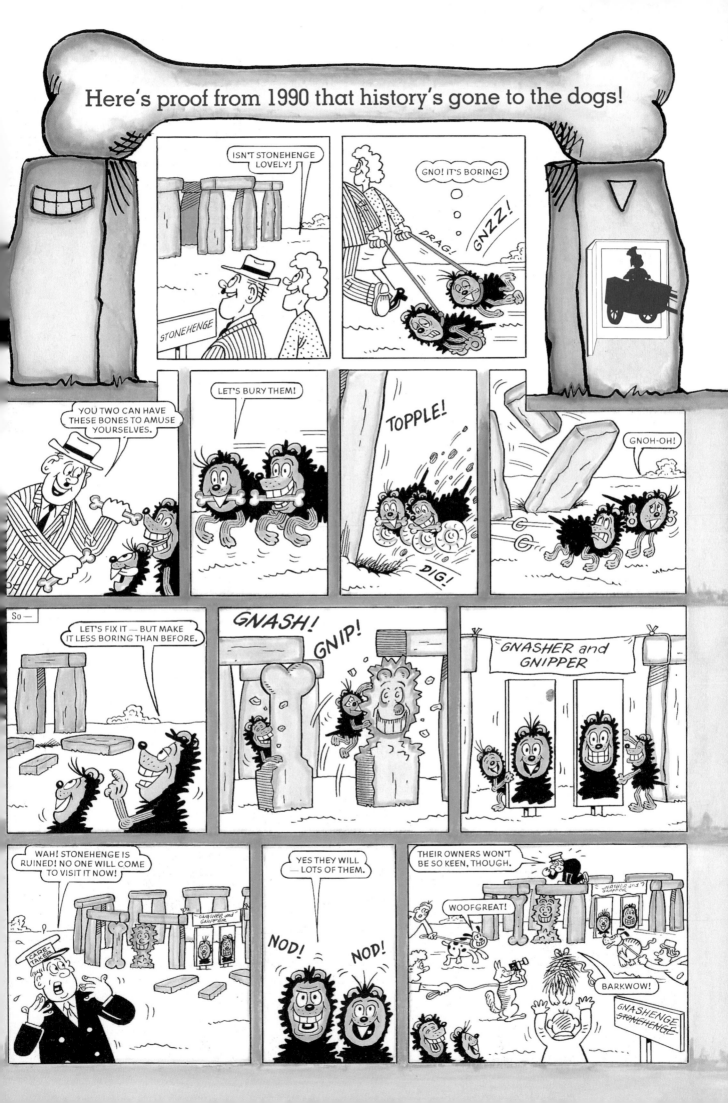

In 1986, The Jocks and The Geordies re-enacted their own version of the Battle of Waterloo — in the local library! Well, they do have a history of being fighting-fit . . . fit for fighting every week!

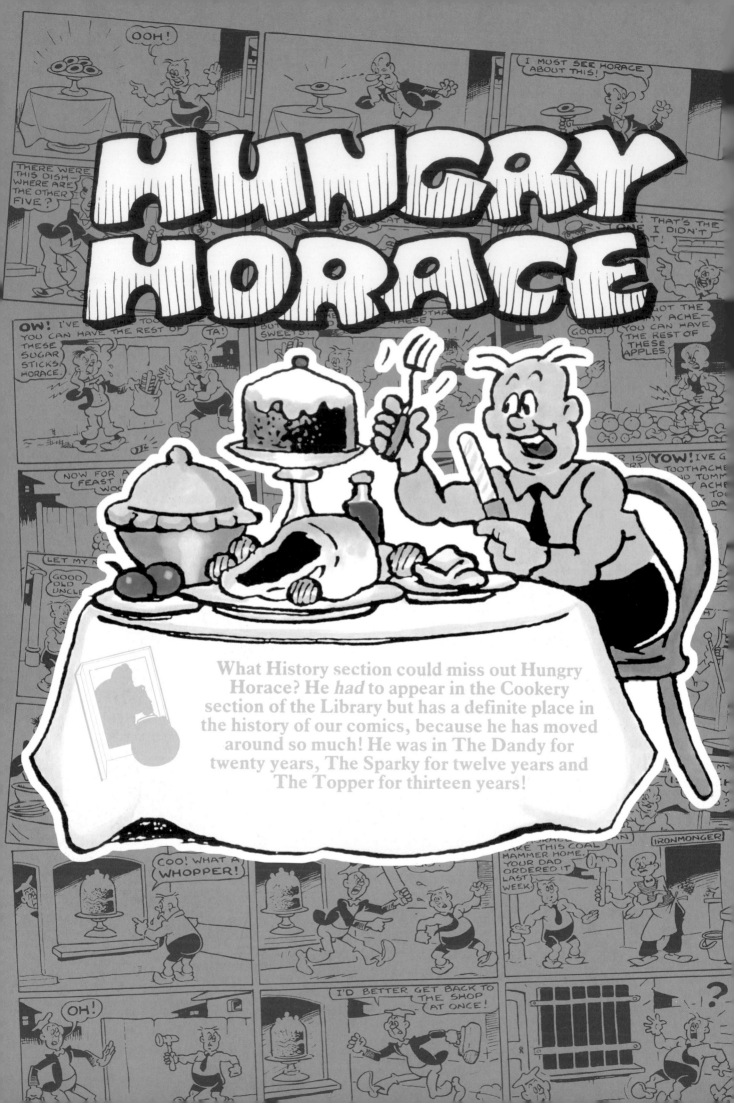

HUNGRY HORACE

What History section could miss out Hungry Horace? He *had* to appear in the Cookery section of the Library but has a definite place in the history of our comics, because he has moved around so much! He was in The Dandy for twenty years, The Sparky for twelve years and The Topper for thirteen years!

PHOTO ALBUM

Do you know this smartly-combed chap who is being photographed? You should recognise him in a flash! Believe it or not, it's . . . well, have a look in the album and you'll see a photo of him, along with other past and present comic chums!

Gulp! Lord Snooty and his pals seem to be in trouble, in this story from The Beano 1962 . . . or have they been framed . . . photoframed, that is!

Who is this?

Dennis the Menace, believe it or not! Have a look at the ten-year-old tale that explains what happened!

Do not adjust your book! These pages are in control of your laughter muscles! Please sit down and be entertained by this part of the Library, which has some weird and wonderful gadgets in its pages, from Lord Snooty's flying saucer through to Charley Brand's pal, Brassneck. Tin Lizzie and Jack Silver are metallic-sounding mirth-makers also waiting for you, if you dare to turn these pages!

...so's yells alerted the janitor, who charged bravely in to quench the flames.

YAHOO!

COOL DOWN, MR SNODGRASS! EVERYTHING'S UNDER CONTROL!

Another soaking meant that Fatso needed more dry clothes.

YOU CAN'T TEACH DRESSED LIKE THAT, MR SNODGRASS GO AND BORROW A DRY COSTUME FROM THE SCHOOL DRAMATIC SOCIETY.

The school play was Westward Ho!—and Fatso's costume raised many a Ho-Ho!

GRR! SHUT UP, YOU LITTLE MONSTERS!

Swotty had got wet and was shivering. He jabbed at the control box.

BRR! I'LL GET BRASSNECK TO B-BRING ME A WARM COAT.

Brassneck went hunting and this was where he spied a suitable coat—in the police station!

YIKE! A THIEF PINCHING MY COAT! HELP! POLICE!

BLEEP! THIS COAT WILL SUIT MY MASTER FINE.

Swotty met up with the metal boy at playtime. But their chit-chat was interrupted—

TA, BRASSNECK!

HOLD IT RIGHT THERE, WATT!

Fatso was going home to change, and a coat was just what he needed to hide his fancy costume.

YOU DON'T MIND IF I BORROW THAT NICE LONG COAT, DO YOU, BOY?

ER—NO, SIR!

The master hadn't noticed the police markings on the shoulders of the coat, but two bobbies did.

STOP! IN THE NAME OF THE LAW!

EH! WHAT? I'VE DONE NOTHING!

Fatso didn't like the look on their faces and he speeded up.

The master was going like a rocket and was too late to see the danger ahead. The road was up, and suddenly he was down—with a Thump!

ROAD UP

YAAARGH!

WOW!

HEY! YOU MUST BE NEEDING SPECS, MATE!

The burly bobbies were set upon locking Fatso up. But the master protested so loudly that they agreed to go back to the school with him.

WE'LL SEE, SIR.

BUT I DIDN'T KNOW IT WAS THE SERGEANT'S COAT OFFICER! A BOY AT SCHOOL GAVE IT TO ME! HONEST!

Swotty couldn't blame Brassneck without giving away the secret of his control box. It was a stroke of luck for him, however, that when Fatso was off looking for his cane, the bobbies marched the rotter away home for punishment.

OH, DEAR! MR SNODGRASS WILL BE DISAPPOINTED.

HO—HO! CHEER UP, SWOTTY! YOUR DAD WON'T WHACK YOU HALF AS HARD AS OLD FATSO WOULD!

TIN LIZZIE

THE chimney in Professor Puffin's study was being swept, and as the sweep thrust his brush up inside it, he was closely watched by the Professor's mechanical servants, Tin Lizzie and Brassribs. They were a strange couple, for they were made completely of metal. Both had amazing mechanical brains, enabling them to do almost anything.

2 — They were good servants and had given the Professor very little trouble — until recently. Somebody had been trying to gain control of Brassribs by sending out wireless signals which affected the butler's works. These signals usually started the butler off on something crazy. And, at this very moment the unknown wireless fiend was busy again.

3 — Sitting at his strange wireless set he twiddled the dials until picture of Brassribs flashed on small screen. "Aha!" he muttered. "Got him!" Immediately a strange thing happened in Puffin's house. Brassribs rushed forward and grabbed the sweep's brush. "Get out of the way!" he rumbled "You're not doing the job properly."

4 — "Golly!" gasped Lizzie. "What's he up to now?" She soon found out — and so did the sweep's mate up on the roof! Brassribs rammed the brush up the chimney with such force that it shot out the top and biffed the sweep's mate smack on the chin. Back he tumbled.

5 — "What's that?" gasped Lizzie as a howl of pain echoed down the chimney. She rushed out of the house to see what was going on — and next moment she found herself lying flat on her face. The sweep had been knocked off the roof by the brush, and he landed on Lizzie.

6 — Lizzie and the two sweeps were furious, and all three went looking for Brassribs. But the butler didn't wait for them. He rushed off up the street, clutching the brush and looking all round him for more chimneys to sweep. His pursuers were soon left well behind.

7 — Brassribs was looking for any kind of chimney, as long as it was sooty. As he clanked madly on he saw a road-roller trundling along with clouds of dirty smoke billowing from the smoke-stack. "Ho-ho! A chimney!" he burbled gleefully. "And it's filthy, too! I'll give it a good clean!"

8 — To the driver's horror, Brassribs leaped aboard and rattled the brush up and down the smoke stack. The butler was brushing so furiously that every downward jab forced a shower of glowing coals from the open fire-box. With a startled howl the driver beat a hasty retreat as the burning coals whizzed round his legs. Brassribs went on sweeping till he decided the smoke-stack was clean. Then off he clanked, chased by an angry Lizzie, who had tracked him down. Meanwhile the red-hot coals were bursting holes in car tyres and melting the tar on the road. What a to-do there was!

Tin Lizzie and Brassribs were robots which featured in The Dandy nearly fifty years ago. However, along with the sci-fi view of a robotic future, have a look at the things we rarely see nowadays, such as a car-battery-powered (wireless) "computer", chimney-sweep, coal-powered road-roller and firemen's "jumping sheet"!

9 — But that was nothing to the panic the butler caused with his next escapade. He found a real whopper of a chimney to sweep — a factory chimney over one hundred feet tall! Lizzie saw him disappear through the factory gates, then he suddenly reappeared, climbing up the iron ladder fixed to the side of the chimney. "Look at that madman!" a passer-by shouted. "He'll kill himself. Call the Fire Brigade to get him down."

10 — Another man nipped into a telephone kiosk and dialled 999 as, step by step, Brassribs climbed up the ladder. The fire engine didn't take long to arrive, but by that time Brassribs had almost reached the top. Then, just as the fire engine roared into the yard, Brassribs got into difficulties. The iron pins holding the top of the ladder to the chimney were old and rusty. His weight proved too much for them. They snapped!

11 — Brassribs hung on with one hand as the ladder swayed backwards, but it was obvious that he couldn't cling on for long. "Bring out the jumping sheet," ordered the Fire Chief. As the firemen rushed to do this, another two of the ladder supports gave way and the ladder sagged further. Scrambling on top of a coke pile, the firemen stretched out the jumping sheet. "Hoi!" yelled the Fire Chief to Brassribs. "Jump!" Brassribs seemed about to refuse, but the ladder lurched, making him drop his brush. He got ready to jump. "That sheet will never hold old Rustyribs." Lizzie gasped.

12 — Lizzie was a true prophet. The butler jumped, and whizzed down at the jumping sheet like a bomb. *Rrrip!* When his great weight hit the sheet, he just went right through it. Then — *Crrunch!* He bored into the middle of the coke heap and disappeared completely.

13 — The firemen gaped at the torn jumping sheet. "It's impossible!" one gasped. "That butler chap must weigh a ton!" Then Lizzie butted in. "Well, don't stand gaping," she hooted. "Let's dig out the silly heap of scrap iron." The astonished firemen fell back and watched in wonder as the metal maid began to dig among the coke where Brassribs had vanished. Five minutes later, when she had moved half of the coke heap aside, she found the butler and dragged him clear.

14 — "Let go my leg!" Brassribs bellowed. "I must sweep the chimney." Lizzie snorted as she dragged him homewards. "You're not sweeping any chimney," she growled. "You're going for a bath." In spite of the butler's protests, Lizzie pegged him to the clothes line and hosed him clean. The man to blame for the butler's crazes watched this, unseen, from over the wall. "Bah!" he growled. "I can't control him properly yet. I must try again." Lizzie and Puffin were due for more trouble soon.

WILLIE'S WHIZZER BROOM

"**W**ILLIE! Run down to the shops and get me a basket of potatoes," called Grandma Meldrum. "Right-oh, Grandma," replied her grandson, Willie, scooping up his marbles. "Just going." He picked up the basket and nipped smartly into the garden shed.

2 — He didn't fancy trudging to the shops. "I'll use my Whizzer Broom," he decided. Willie's Whizzer Broom looked quite ordinary, but actually it was a magic broom. When Willie sat astride it and pressed a hidden button it whisked him off to the world of the future.

3 — *Whoosh!* Off went Willie with h basket and, quick as winking, he four himself landing in the future in front of row of food machines. "I'm in luck Willie whooped. "I'll have a bob's wor of grub from one of these que machines. It'll be better than spuds."

4 — He chose a machine marked "Grade B. Light workers," and pushed his shilling into the slot. Bells clanged, buzzers buzzed and his picture flashed on to a television screen. "Cheat! Arrest this boy!" blared a voice from a loudspeaker. "Gosh!" Willie gasped. "A shilling's no use in this contraption. I think I'd better beat it." He'd never had a better idea, for the noise made by the machine had attracted an old enemy of his.

5 — This was Sergeant Fuzz, a policeman of the future. Willi had made a fool of him before, and Sergeant Fuzz didn't lik being fooled, so now that he had a good excuse to arrest Willi he didn't mean to miss the chance. Willie was haring off at to speed when the bobby pulled a couple of levers beside th pavement. A moment later Willie noticed although he wa running hard, he wasn't moving forward one little bit!

6 — "Wow!" he gasped. "What's going on here? You'd think the pavement was moving backwards." Suddenly he realised what he had said, and he looked down at his feet. The pavement *was* moving backwards — and he was being carried into Sergeant Fuzz's clutches! "Got you, you rogue!" the sergeant roared, clamping a heavy hand on Willie's shoulder. "Trying to steal food is a very serious offence." "I wasn't trying to steal it," Willie protested. "I put my money in the rotten old machine."

7 — "A likely story!" Fuzz grated. "Where's the coin you used?" Willie fumbled in his pocket. "I — I must have dropped it," he stammered. "Look! There's an old gent picking it up!" This was a stroke of luck for Willie, for the old gentleman was a coin collector. "Wait, Sergeant," the old gentleman said. "This coin is over five hundred years old. It's very valuable. I will buy it from the boy, then he will have enough money to get food." And he thrust a fistful of coins into Willie's hand.

— Willie's new-found friend must have been an important chap in this world of the future, for Sergeant Fuzz saluted smartly. "As you wish, Citizen Glook," he growled, then in a mutter he warned Willie, "but I'll get you yet!" Willie was mighty relieved at his escape and decided it was time he collected his grub and went. So, while Citizen Glook led Sergeant Fuzz away, Willie tried all the slot machines.

9 — But it was strange "food" that he got in exchange for his money. The food of the future looked like large-sized pills, sealed in a plastic container, and each pill was a whole meal in itself. "Oh, well," Willie decided. "I suppose they must be all right or they wouldn't be on sale." Off he strolled with his basket loaded to the brim, and the sight of so much grub brought envious glares from three boys whom he passed.

10 — "Want some?" Willie asked. The boys did! Who would miss the chance of free grub? But it wasn't just a case of Willie handing over the pills — oh no! He made the boys play at marbles to win the grub. But the boys had some jolly queer ideas about marbles.

11 — They didn't play the same way as Willie did. They put their own striped marbles into a spring gun and fired them at Willie's marbles, but even that didn't help them to beat Willie. He was in absolutely unbeatable form, and in no time at all he scooped the pool.

12 — "Hard luck, chaps," he cheerfully remarked, gathering up his opponents' striped marbles. The boys from the future turned dolefully away with the one marble they had won from Willie, then the boy who had won it did a surprising thing. He took a bite at it!

13 — "Wah!" His roar of pain and anger made Willie swing round. "What does the silly ass think he's doing?" he gasped. Then it suddenly became clear to him. These boys from the future had been playing marbles with their dinners, and they must have thought Willie was doing the same! Now the angry trio turned on him. "It's time I made myself scarce," Willie muttered. He hopped astride the Whizzer Broom and pressed the secret stud in the handle. *Whoosh!* Off he went.

14 — But before he was carried out of range the boy with the sore teeth gained some revenge by pinging Willie's ear with his marble. Still, Willie reckoned it was worth having his ear pinged to gain all that grub because he had a smashing dinner — two striped pills and three red ones! Then he sat back, full to the tonsils, and beamed at Grandma and Grandad, who stared uncertainly at their strange meal. "Lovely grub!" he breathed, but somehow he felt Grandma and Grandad preferred spuds!

Man-eating octopus plants, Red Indians, Boombangers and Bogglers

CURLY PERKINS was having the time of his life in the wacky world of Marsuvia, far off in Outer Space. He had been brought here in a space ship by his happy-go-lucky Marsuvian friend, Jack Silver.

Today the lads were journeying half-way across Marsuvia to visit one of Jack's uncles. They were crossing the wild Zoggi jungle when Curly felt the space scooter engine shudder and splutter..

I'LL LAND AND TAKE A LOOK AT THE ENGINE.

Before the engine conked out, Jack spotted a clearing and landed safely.

GOSH! WHAT A FANTASTIC PLACE! I HOPE THERE'S NOTHING DANGEROUS HERE.

WE'LL GET ON OUR WAY AGAIN AS SOON AS I PUT THE ENGINE RIGHT.

Jack Silver found the fault and set about repairing it. Curly, meanwhile, wandered off to take a look at this strange, outlandish jungle.

ONE OF THE FIZZ BATTERY CONNECTIONS IS BROKEN. I'LL SOON FIX IT.

HEY! THAT FUNNY ANIMAL LOOKS FRIENDLY. I'LL CALL IT OVER.

YOO-HOO! HOW WOULD YOU LIKE A BISCUIT?

BOOM! BOOM!

What happened next was astonishing. The startled animal began thumping its tail against a hollow plant. Loud Booms echoed through the jungle.

HEY! WHAT ARE YOU DOING THAT FOR? HAVE YOU GOT AN ITCHY TAIL?

Curly didn't know it, but he had started up some trouble! The funny creature was a Boombanger, and lots of them were used as watchdogs. The booming signal was heard by other Boombangers and relayed all the way to a village in the jungle.

BOOM! BOOM!

OOGLY-BOOGLY! BANGER-CLANGER!

The big chief's Boombanger made sure he got the message!

YOWEE-WOWEE! TOOTSIE-WOOTSIE!

BONK!

Within moments a war party of Bogglers was storming out of the village.

RUNNIM-FUNNIM! GHARGIM-BARGIM!

It was poor Jack Silver whom they found first. The poor lad had barely time to let out a howl before he was overpowered.

BONKIM-CLONKIM!

GIFFIM-BIFFIM!

GOOD! I'VE FIXED THE TROUBLE— ZEOWL!

Curly gasped when he heard all the noise, but he was smart enough to keep hidden when he saw the mighty mob who had captured his pal.

SPOTTEM-CAUGHTEM!

YO-HO-HO-HO!

HELP!

OH, NO! THAT FUNNY BOOMING THING MUST HAVE BROUGHT THOSE GUYS! I'VE LANDED JACK IN TROUBLE THIS TIME!

Taking great care not to be seen, Curly followed the Bogglers to their village. What were the ugly-mugs going to do next, that was what he wanted to know?

The two head Bogglers untied Jack and shoved him towards the gate of the stockade. On the other side Curly could see a funny-looking plant moving about.

I DON'T LIKE THE LOOK OF THIS.

WOOOGO CHEERUMHO!

Curly Perkins sees them all, in this exotic Dandy tale from 1973!

The Library's SPORT section has Dennis the Menace playing croquet with Walter, and Desperate Dan playing darts as only Dan can! There are no records being broken, though — except maybe for laughter!

THE GREAT BEANO v DANDY
FOOTBALL MATCH.
(The Dandy 1991)

Little Ivy the Terrible, a Beano star since 1985, must surely be the oldest toddler around — she can't "weight" to grow up and do all the things adults do!

This hairy-chinned school-teacher appeared for a short time in

The Dandy in the mid 'fifties — BIG BEARDIE by name. He's the one on the left, without the horns!

CROQUET ... OR WAS IT GOLF?

Dennis the Menace has always liked playing sports and games with Walter ...

'WEAVE' HAD ENOUGH!

PARTY ANIMAL!

WALTER GETS A NEW...ER...SOOT!

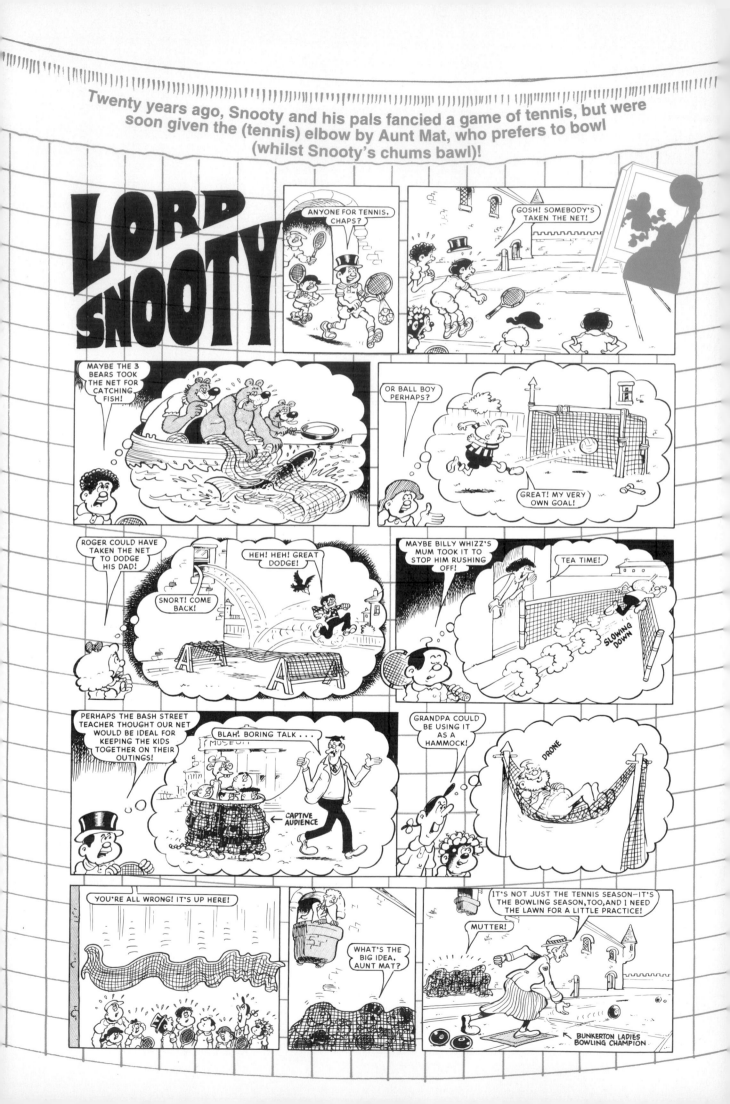

Ball Boy has rarely been "booked", but he's on this page today trying to show you a "novel" way to score a goal in not quite "textbook" form, thanks to someone who keeps moving the goalposts!

The Dandy story, "Strange Hill School" isn't really Science Fiction, nor is it Magic; it's nothing to do with Animals either, or Cookery — that's why it's in the Sport Section! Well, it's about a bat . . . and there's a net!

The beasts of Bamboo Town were umpteen years ahead of their time — they had adverts on their chests long before sports goods manufacturers hit on the idea!

HUH! THEM DARTS ARE FAR TOO SMALL FOR ME!

POOR OLD DAN! HE CAN'T EVEN HIT THE BOARD!

GUESS I NEED A REAL OUT-SIZE DART-BOARD IF I'M GONNA BE A CHAMPION AT THIS GAME!

GEE! LOOK AT THAT STEP-LADDER!

TELEGRAPH POLES, BAYONETS AND OSTRICH FEATHERS! GOSH, MY DARTS ARE GONNA BE SWELL!

MUSIC

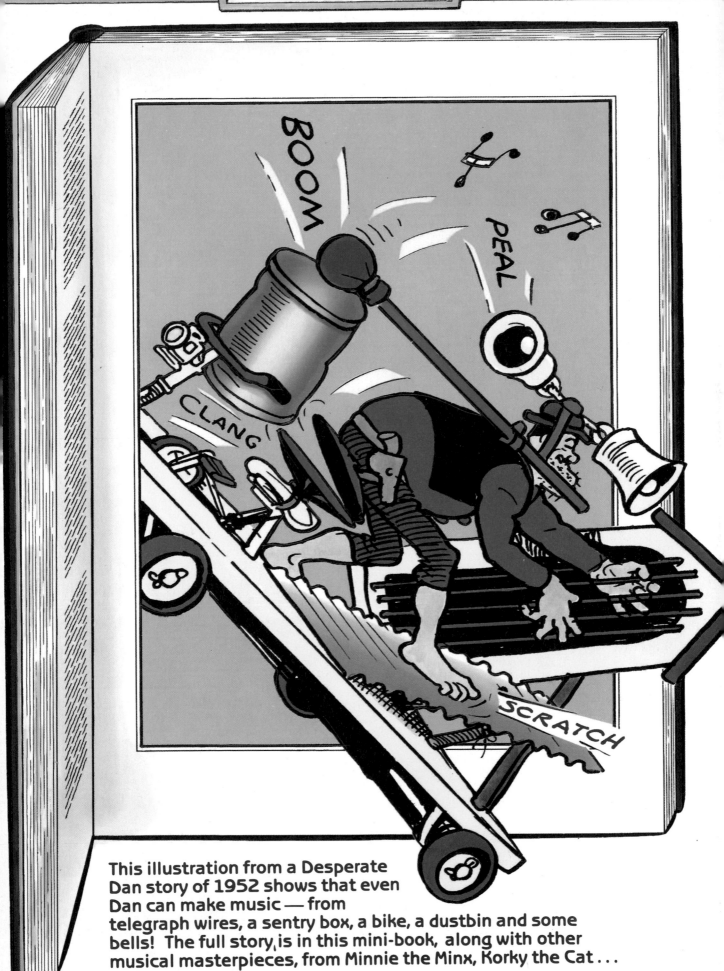

This illustration from a Desperate Dan story of 1952 shows that even Dan can make music — from telegraph wires, a sentry box, a bike, a dustbin and some bells! The full story is in this mini-book, along with other musical masterpieces, from Minnie the Minx, Korky the Cat . . .

In the early '50s, music-making wasn't quite as sophisticated as it is today — as long as you had a piano, a set of drums, Korky the Cat, a sea-lion and an octopus!

This page wasn't going in the History or Geography Books, or the Cookery Book. It should've perhaps gone in the Anatomy Book, or even the Doomsday Book, but as it's all about germs singing a lullaby, it's in the Music Book!

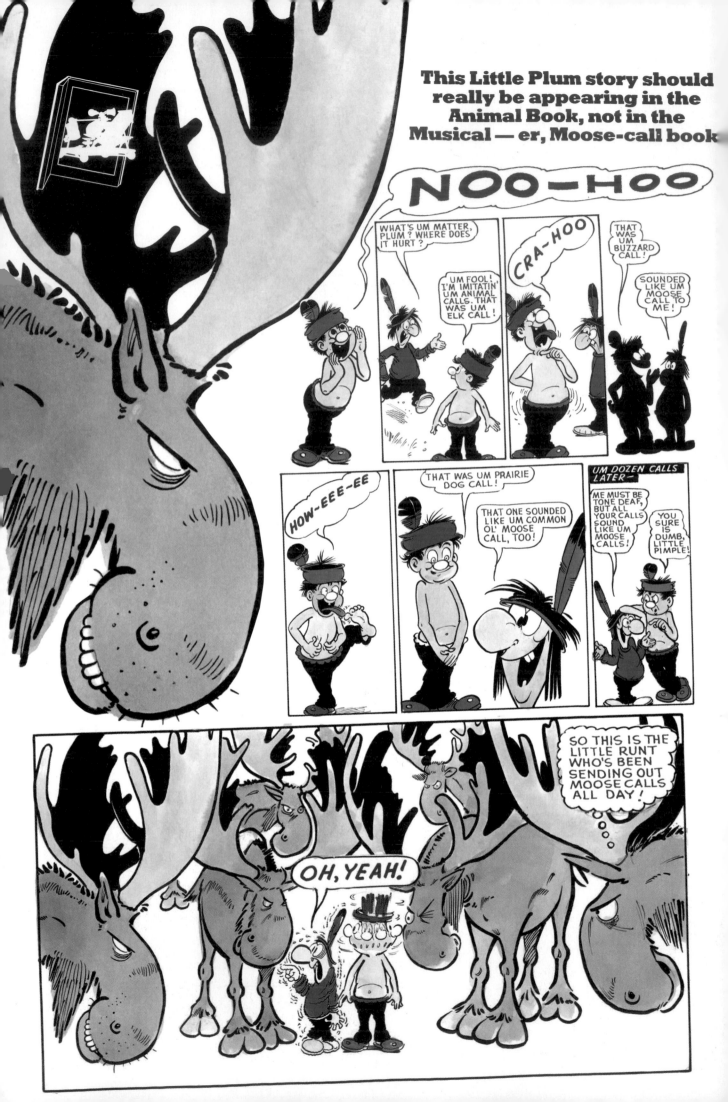

GEOGRAPHY

The GEOGRAPHY section of the Library shows a slice of life and laughter outside Britain that The Beano and The Dandy have highlighted over the years.

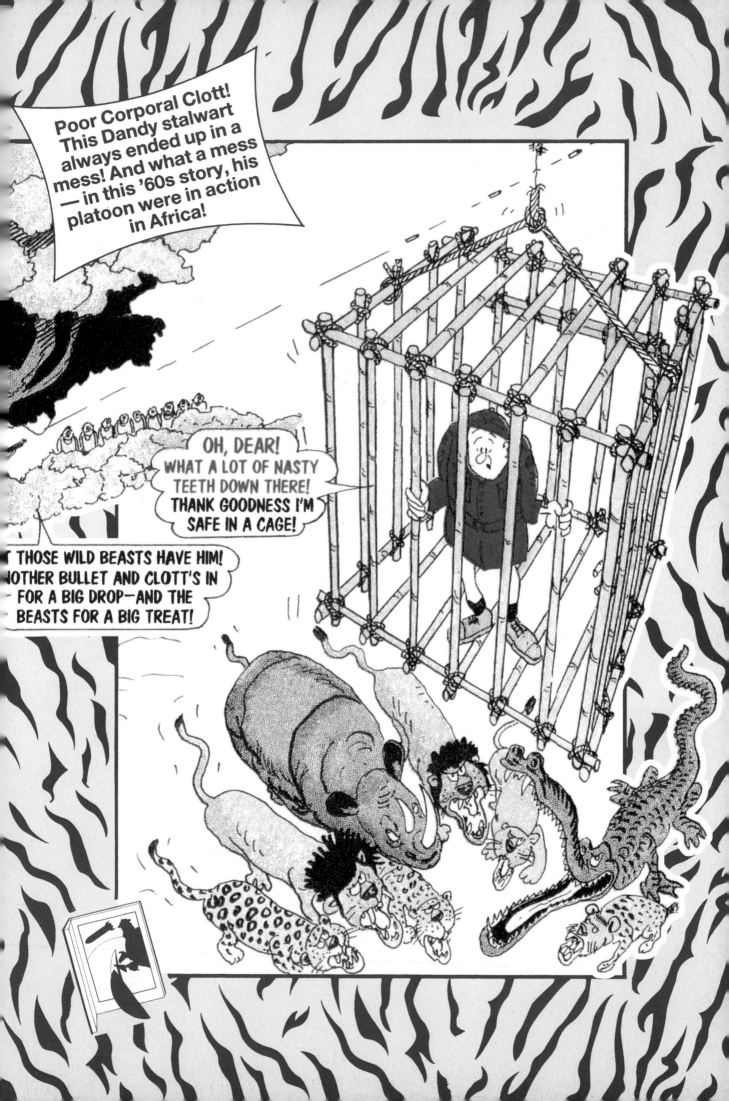

...rtled by the strange little attackers which ...mbo controlled so skilfully, the tiger fled ...o the high grass and vanished.

Jumbo at once brought back his models.

TAKE HIM TO MY DOCTOR IMMEDIATELY... NOW WE MUST FIND THAT TIGER!

For an hour they searched for the tiger. Then suddenly the elephant stood on a rotting log . . .

Dazed and winded, Jumbo began to scramble to his feet. Suddenly he became aware of a pair of bright yellow eyes fixing him with a cruel stare!

ONE OF MY FIELD GUNS! IT MUST HAVE BEEN THROWN OUT OF THE HOWDAH WITH ME. I H-HOPE IT'S LOADED!

Jumbo grabbed the gun. It WAS loaded — with a small stink-bomb.

And as the tiger sprang at him the boy fired.

The big animal reeled back, snarling, so strong was the stench in his nostrils. Then it turned tail and fled blindly —

— straight over the edge of a ravine!

HE WILL HARM MY PEOPLE NO MORE — THANKS TO YOU, GENERAL JUMBO.

The next tiger hunt was not exactly what the Rajah expected. But he enjoyed every moment of it . . .

YOU CONTROL THE MODEL HUNTERS, SIR. I'LL CONTROL THE TIGER!

Stunned by its fall, the tiger was easily trussed up by the ...earers and carried to the Rajah's private zoo.

PHEW! THAT TIGER HUNT CERTAINLY WAS HAIR-RAISING. BUT LET'S HAVE ANOTHER ONE RIGHT AWAY, SIR!

ALL ABOARD THE DANGER BUS!

It is the summer of 1940. A ferry-boat carrying a bus-load of children from Felladale School has been swept across the English Channel by a fierce storm. Now the youngsters and their teacher, Mr Kean, hav landed in German-occupie France. As the bus, nicknamed "Nellie", climb the bumpy track from the sea-shore, a German sent appears . . .

But soon an officer and the sentry were in pursuit.

With tyres howling, the old bus swervec round a corner into open countryside and the pursuing Germans lost sigh of it for a few moments.

Some time later, Mr Kean spotted a lone British airman dropping by parachute dangerously close to a German patrol. He sent the bus crashing through a fence.

But Mr Kean had all his wits about him. Skilfully he steered the lurching bus down under the dark arch of the bridge. He was not a moment too soon.

YOU'VE FOOLED THE JERRIES, MR KEAN! THEY'VE GONE STRAIGHT ON OVER THE BRIDGE!

He drove straight a the patrol, who had t quickly dive out of th way!

Close your eyes if you don't like insects! These giant ants and wasps are from a Dandy Book 1969 story called "The Island Of Monsters", set somewhere in the Pacific Ocean.

ANATOMY

BAREFOOT BILL (DANDY BOOK 1970)

THE BOY WITH IRON HANDS (DANDY 1959)

TOOTHY TIM (DANDY BOOK 1949)

THE BYRD BRAINS (DANDY BOOK 1984)

THE BOY WHO LIVES IN A BARREL (BEANO 1951)

FLEETFOOT JACK (DANDY 1954)

POOR OLD NOSEY (DANDY 1946)

TOM TUM (DANDY 1978)

THE KING WITH THE CAULIFLOWER CONK (BEANO BOOK 1959)

HANDY SANDY (BEANO 1942)

FERGUS OF THE FORTY FACES (DANDY 1950)

BUCKTOOTH — THE BOY WHO LIVES IN A BARREL

THE FINEST EARS IN TEXAS (BEANO BOOK 1958)

LONGLEGS, THE DESERT WILD BOY (BEANO 1955)

FREDDY FLIPPERFEET (BEANO 1942)

DOLLY DIMPLE (BEANO BOOK 1948)

THE VENGEANCE OF ONE-EYE (BEANO 1957)

Both The Beano and The Dandy have often used everything from heads to toes in their various story titles — see the examples above — so the following collection of bodily parts should exercise your laughter muscles!

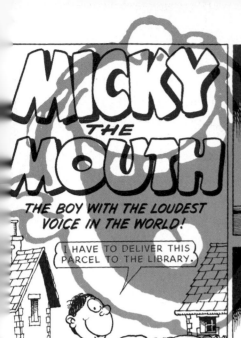

This 1964 tale of wily Winker Watson and his brother Wallie shows they always wanted to outwit each other in a wayward war of wangles!

IF Winker Watson hadn't had a young brother named Wallie, he couldn't have earned a bonus for keeping him out of trouble, could he? That was Wallie's thought when Winker received the cash, and young Wallie reasoned that the money rightly belonged to him. So he decided to fight for his rights.

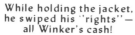

Winker didn't know it yet, but Wallie had already thought of a way of getting his hands on that money.

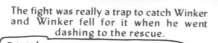

The fight was really a trap to catch Winker and Winker fell for it when he went dashing to the rescue.

In the challenge match that followed, Wallie urged Winker on—and held his jacket for him.

While holding the jacket, he swiped his "rights"— all Winker's cash!

Winker got on to Wallie's trail in a desperate hurry and the trail took him all the way to the village.

Winker knew the banker and went dashing in to see what Wallie had done with the loot.

Why all the halfpennies? Winker was baffled — but at least he could nab them now.

Whoopee! The loot had fallen right into Winker's hands!

At last Winker had discovered Wallie's reason for obtaining all those halfpennies. Though Winker had the loot, he could not lift it! And Wallie was off to bring his gang!

NO. 13

Make no bones about it, it's useful having a skeleton for an uncle! Boris and Uncle Boney are from October 1990 Beano.

KNOW YOUR COVER CHARACTERS

If you haven't been reading The Beano or The Dandy for the past 60 years or so, there are some characters you may not recognise, so here is a cover identification parade!

DIMPLES 32
CHIPS 33
DESPERATE DAN 34
WALTER THE SOFTY 35
KORKY THE CAT 36
BIG EGGO 37
DANNY (Leader of the Bash Street Kids) 38
DENNIS THE MENACE 39
LITTLE PLUM 40
MINNIE THE MINX 41
WILFRID (The Bash Street Kids) 42
GNASHER (DENNIS' DOG) 43
WINKER WATSON 44
CORPORAL CLOTT 45
BILLY WHIZZ 46
EGG HEAD 48
JONAH 49
HAM 49
BRASSNECK 50
CHARLIE BRAND 51
LORD SNOOTY 52
TEACHER (The Bash Street Kids) 53
SIR COWARD DE CUSTARD 54
CALAMITY JAMES 55
ALEXANDER LEMMING (JAMES' PET) 56
SIDNEY (The Jocks and The Geordies) 57
GRANDPA 58
BUSTER (Biffo's Pal) 59
BIFFO THE BEAR 60

DOOMSDAY BOOK

There are certain characters who are almost too dangerous to have in a Library — That's why they've earned themselves a special place in the corner (a very dark corner). Try to be brave when you open the DOOMSDAY BOOK!

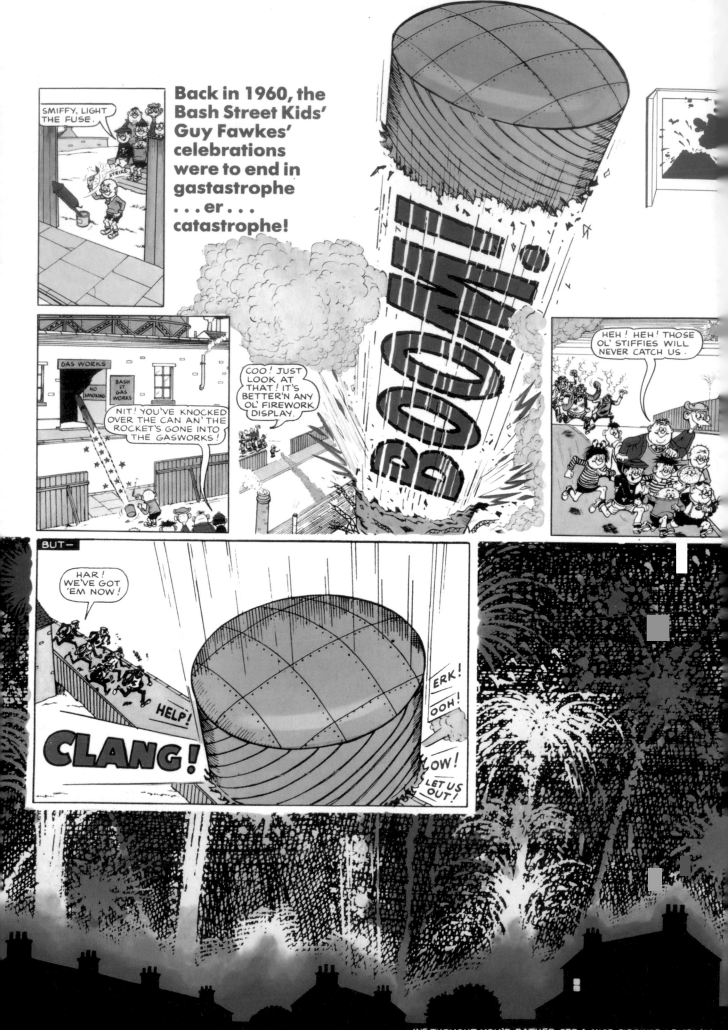

Molly has been a pest to her parents over 400 times in the pages of The Dandy! Here's one of those pesty times, 'specially for the Doomsday Book!

MAGIC

The MAGIC era of The Beano and Dandy Library has been with us right from the early days of the two comics — and it'll never disappear as long as there are characters like Wuzzy Wiz and Baggy Pants around to cause trouble. When the

This early '70s Bash Street Kids tale shows that the "magic" of comics will never disappear!

WHEN TEACHER WAS A LITTLE BOY, HE DIDN'T WANT TO BE A TEACHER —

WHAT WILL I BE WHEN I GROW UP?

THAT'S MY BOY!

TEACHER'S DAD

THAT TRICK SHOULD IMPRESS THE MAGICIANS. NOW I MUST GO AND ASK THE HEADMASTER FOR PERMISSION TO SIT MY MAGICIAN'S EXAM THIS AFTERNOON.

BUT, WHILE TEACHER'S GONE —

COO! WHAT A NICE LITTLE KITTEN. I MUST HAVE IT FOR A PET.

STAFF ROOM

KITTEN? THAT BOY MUST BE A NIT!

BACK IN CLASS IIB —

PUSS! PUSS! COME ON, PUSS!

BASH ST. MAGICIANS' CLUB

I WONDER WHAT COULD HAVE HAPPENED TO MY RABBIT?

FAKER!

RAZZ!

BOO!

BACK AT SCHOOL —

GURR! SO YOU TOOK MY RABBIT. GNASH!

YOUR RABBIT? ERK! RUN FOR IT, KIDS!

TREE →

HILL ↓

RABBIT BURROWS →

POND ↓

HIDE IN BEHIND THIS CURTAIN OR WHATEVER IT IS!

SUDDENLY, THE LIGHTS GO ON AND —

GRR! SNARL!

ERK! LET'S GET OUT OF HERE — FAST!

LOOK, IT'S THAT TEACHER FELLOW AGAIN. HE MUST BE GOING TO SHOW US ANOTHER TRICK.

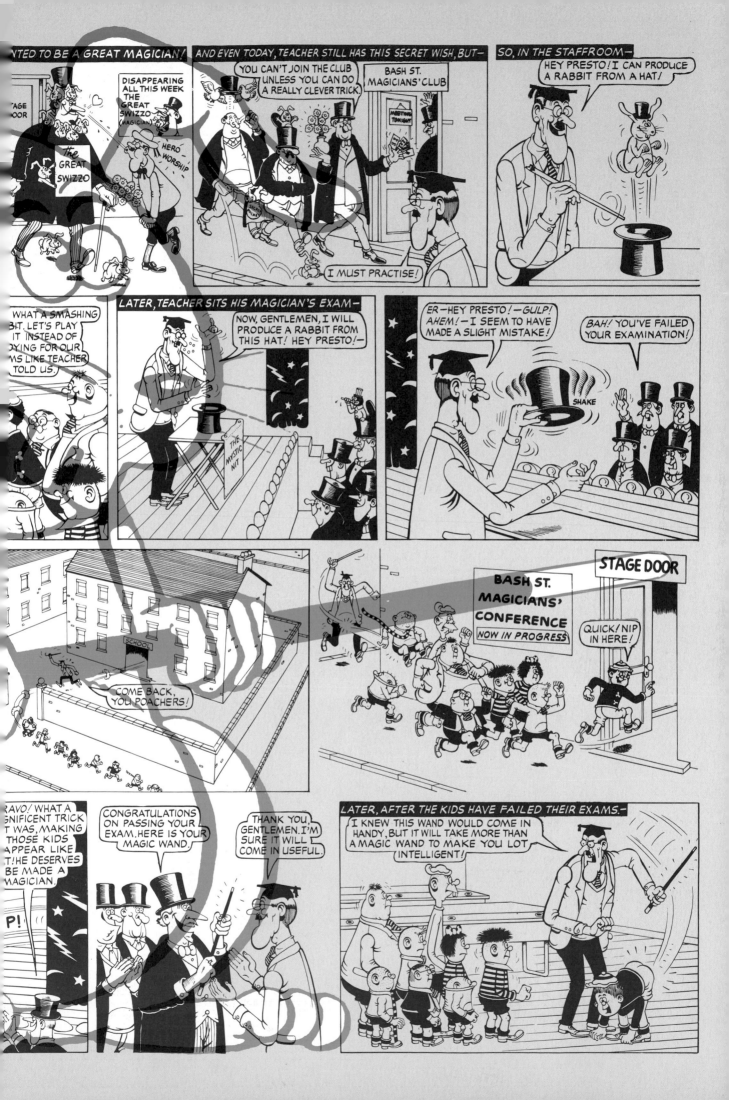

Jimmy hopped up on the running board and peppered the driver with questions. "Was it a big fire? Where was it? Gosh! I'd like to see a really big fire . . ."

To the sound of thunderous roars from a vast audience, the whole outfit landed slap in the middle of a chariot race taking place in a vast amphitheatre. The Patch had whisked Jim and his friends back almost 2000 years to Ancient Rome!

Nero, who was Emperor of Rome at the time, was livid at his afternoon's fun being spoiled.

There won't be many readers who have an Eastern magician like —
MY PAL BAGGY PANTS from The Dandy 1958

My name is Johnny Grant, folks. But maybe it should be Johnny Grunt, for me and my pal, Baggy Pants, were snoring and grunting like fun when a burglar broke into our house.

We woke up to see him sweeping his loot into a bag, and Baggy nearly had a fit. Baggy's magic carpet and his book of magic spells were being swiped!

My little magician leaped into a model car and squeaked a magic spell. "Little car, help me in my need — Find the police at greatest speed!"

Baggy touched the gear lever, but he must have touched it the wrong way. For when the car roared into magic life, it reversed slap-bang against the wall!

Baggy didn't give up, though. He leaped astride a book, once again chanting a spell. "Bake boil, stew, fry — Flap your pages, start to fly!"

Alas, this was Baggy's unlucky day.

Instead of growing ... the book sprouted ... and began to prance ... horse.

Still it trotted away after the burglar, who was lumbering down the stairs. It couldn't have been used to walking on legs, however, for it brought disaster to my Eastern wizard.

The book stumbled over its own feet, and shot Baggy off ... spine. My wee magician landed on the banister and went flyi... down on his tummy.

The burglar opened the front door while Baggy was zipping down the rail like a high-speed toboggan. He was going so fast that he hadn't had time to think.

Swish — bump — plunk! Poor Baggy bounced on the rubber mat and sailed head first into the bottle of milk on the doorstep.

I had to laugh. You'd laugh, too, at the sight of the wee man stamping around with his head jammed in a bottle. But what about the burglar? Baggy's luck will have to change if he's to catch him.

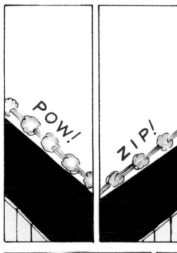

ANIMALS

The ANIMALS section of
the Library is one of the most
important areas — where else would
you find cats, bears and ostriches speaking
perfect English?! Perhaps the question is; who taught
Korky, Biffo and the others to speak? Only The Beano and
The Dandy know the answer!

Those mice really bring Korky down to size in this Dandy front page story from 1951.

KORKY the CAT

KORKY HAS A MAGIC MIXTURE TO SPOIL EACH MOUSE'S APPETITE. AND THOUGH HIS LITTLE PLAN GOES WRONG, HE FINDS THE MIXTURE WORKS ALL RIGHT!

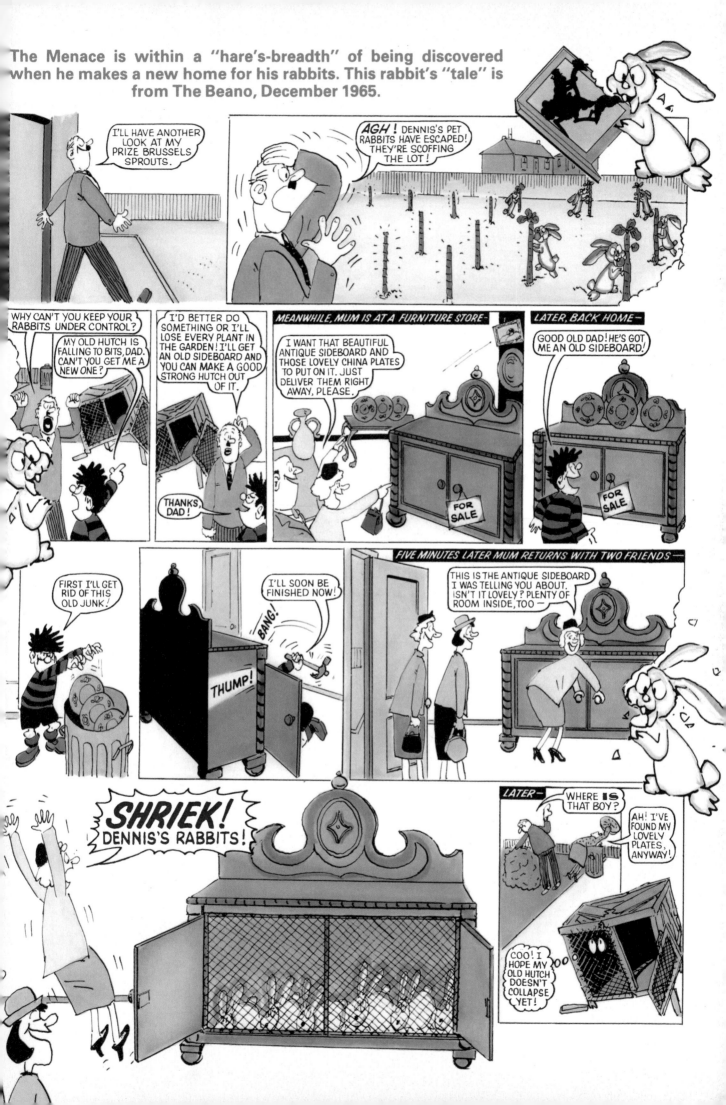

This tale for the Animal Book is more of a *tail* — tail feathers, in fact! Little Plum had a little trouble renewing Chiefy's head-dress in The Beano back in 1958